Chapter One

Space . . . a blue-black softness as far as the eye could see, as far as the mind could imagine or the heart conceive. No movement or sound disturbed the darkness, and the still silence was peaceful.

Then the great Oneness of it all gathered itself into a single point, and breathed – and out from that point there flew a handful of bright stars. They scattered throughout the darkness, spinning and rolling far and wide. For a while they twinkled joyfully at each other, the joy beaming lines of light between them. Those light lines joined the stars together like dot-to-dot drawings in the darkness. As more and more lines were formed, the shapes of twelve different creatures began to emerge.

All this time, more stars were flying out of the point of oneness. Some of them were brilliant suns with others, less bright, spinning in orbit around them.

When the twelve drawings were complete, the Oneness smiled hugely with love at these first creatures of creation, and a vast warm pleasure contained them all.

For a while, the twelve dot-to-dot creatures were suspended in space. Without movement or breath, they felt hollow inside as though something needed to be different.

Not far away, one of the smaller stars was spinning wildly, like a humming top out of control, a whirling ball of light. Searching for stability, it began circling in a steady orbit round one of the brighter suns. Its spinning slowed down and, feeling safer, it began to change.

At first its light dimmed, condensing into mist. Gradually the mist became more solid, and a life was born within and around it to take care of its changing. That life we might call Nature, and Nature surrounded the misty globe, holding it softly within herself so that life could grow however it wanted.

The twelve starry creatures felt drawn towards Nature, sensing that she could help them grow too. As they approached the little globe, they shrank, and were soon embedded in Nature's enclosing light. There they slept, quietly growing into the life of this tiny planet.

The light of the sun rippled over its steadily rolling surface, bringing day after night, over and over. Nature felt hills and valleys forming in the surface, with clouds and rivers and sea. And she gladly grew new plants and trees, which flowered abundantly.

There came a day when the planet was ready for the twelve creatures in its surface to wake up. The first to open its eyes was a little sheep-like animal, a ram, standing on Nature's new grass vibrating with the energy of his life.

He was not a ram of the usual kind, but thinner and more sprightly, and he grew the most wonderful glittering horns curled round the sides of his head. The space within each of those horns was filled with a universe of stars that shone and sparkled beside his head, but because these horns blocked his vision on either side, his was a world of grass and sky, and he could only see what was in front of him.

He sniffed the air experimentally, decided it was good and breathed in deeply. Feeling new energy tingling through his little body, he leaped and skipped with joy to be alive. Then he paused because he could feel an emptiness in his stomach, and he reached his mouth down to taste the new blades of grass. The grass was cool and wonderful, and he ate until his stomach was ready to digest its first meal. It was then that the ram realised that his eyelids felt heavy, wanting to close, and he instantly folded his legs down on the ground, falling asleep as he did so. So interested had he been in his own experience, he had failed to notice that he was not alone.

Nearby was a lying-down cow-shape, sleeping peacefully. This creature had grown solid slowly. Slowly the ribs and lungs had formed, and then a stomach to receive its food. And then another stomach formed for added security to make sure that the food was well digested. The head became firmer, forehead as hard as wood, and the soft face radiating gentle strength. At last, thick, close fur covered the body in a smooth earthy brown coat, curly on the forehead and tufted at the end of the tail. The legs, however, were slow to form, preferring the safety of ground rather than the uncertainty of being cow.

All this time, the cow-shape had been sleeping, but now Nature decided it was time for it to wake and sent a little breeze through the flowers growing near the head. One of the bobbing flowers tickled the large soft nose, and the cow sneezed, waking herself at last. Her large brown eyes regarded the surrounding growth with gentle pleasure, and she began to eat what she could reach, curling her tongue lazily round tufts of grass and munching comfortably. But Nature hadn't finished disturbing this peaceful scene.

II

Over the hill tumbled two bright children, holding hands and looking in all directions as fast as they could turn their heads. One of them was chattering constantly about all he saw, as though telling was an essential part of seeing. His twin was more contemplative and quiet, and sometimes the boy dug her in the ribs for a response. It was the sparkling horns that attracted the children to the sleeping ram, and they ran over to see what was there.

"Look, Sister," cried the boy, "what wonderful horns he has! What shall I call him? – I know – Aries." "Come on, Aries!" he shouted, trying to wake the ram, "Why are you sleeping in the daytime?"

The girl child examined the horns curiously, fascinated by the stars inside them.

"Oh, look, Sister!" said the boy again, "there's another one, but it's different."

He pulled at her hand and they ran over to inspect the quietly munching cow.

"Hello – um – Taurus!" he said, naming her firmly. The cow made no response, so he bent down and smiled into her face. "What are you eating?" he asked.

Taurus realised she would have to answer this child, and slowly lifted her head to look at him. Her big eyes gazed at his young face. Then she looked at Sister but still no words formed in her mind. Finally her reply was to blink at the grass and flowers she had been eating.

Sister spoke at last. "You're eating these flowers and grass, aren't you, Taurus?" she said.

Taurus breathed at her gratefully, and would have begun a reply, but Brother couldn't wait that long, and tugged Sister back to Aries to see if Aries would be more responsive than Taurus the cow.

"Come on, Aries! Come and play with us!"

Aries heard the invitation to play and opened his eyes, instantly awake. He leaped up all in one movement, and stood four-square where he had landed. The children began to giggle. In front of him, Aries saw the green grass and a hill, but where was the person who had called him? He leaped up again and landed facing a different direction. This time he saw the twins, and with a gasp of surprise he leaped backwards, all four feet at once. The children thought the ram's jumping was so funny that, by now, they were laughing aloud. Aries frowned because he didn't understand the joke. He stepped towards them, his head well forward to reach them sooner than his cautious legs would allow.

"Who are you?" he demanded suddenly, "What do you mean 'play'?"

Now it was Brother's turn to step back. Aries' frown looked quite fierce for a moment, but it faded quickly and Brother's natural friendliness returned.

"We're Gemini," he said brightly. "Twins. This is my Sister. Do you know Taurus over there? Shall we play exploring? Have you been over the hill?"

At every question Aries had opened his mouth to reply, but couldn't get a word in edgeways. At last he had so many replies backing up to be spoken, that his head became confused. He shook it to try to clear the mess, and the sight of those horns flashing through the air so shocked the children that they darted out of the way. As they were no longer in front of him, Aries was unable to see them in the narrow view he had between his big horns.

He called out, "Hey, wait for me, I was just going to say . . ."

In fact, the Gemini twins had just dodged sideways, and now stood looking at him from the side. As he couldn't see them past the horn, Aries assumed they had gone and left him, and he was so disappointed, he hung his head sadly.

"I only wanted to say . . . ," he repeated, "Bother, I've forgotten what I was going to say! And now they've gone," he added crossly, kicking the ground hard. "Ouch!" he exclaimed in surprise.

Aries looked at his foot curiously. "That hurt!" he said with interest.

Gemini laughed again and, hearing them, Aries looked round delighted that they had not gone. Then he frowned again.

"There's no need to laugh," he shouted crossly, "it's not funny!" But the twins were so light-hearted, suddenly Aries too could see the funny side, and he even managed to giggle a bit himself. At last their laughing calmed down, and Brother said:

"If you've hurt yourself, we could take you to see Mother. She might be able to make it better."

"Who's Mother?"

"She's a lady we met, just the other side of that hill. She's always holding her Baby. They're called Cancer. She's very nice and she's good at looking after people. Come on, we'll show you." Both children ran back up the hill they had come from, expecting Aries to follow. Aries tilted his head to one side considering what new wonders there might be over that hill. Then, with a decisive burst of energy, he dashed off after the twins.

Taurus sighed contentedly now that peace had returned to the little valley, and she began to munch on the grass she had already eaten. This would prepare it well for the second stomach, which would then make it into even better food for her large body.

Chapter Two

Over the hill there was another green valley. Through the lush grassy meadow flowed a stream with ferns and flowers growing along its banks. There on a large stone, sat a rounded motherly woman, singing to her little baby. Her voice was warm and mellow, singing of safety and loving arms. It was a sweet song about how much she loved her Baby, and the stream trickling past accompanied her with its own song. Baby was asleep, sighing every now and then in a dream of contentment.

Suddenly, their peacefulness was broken by a shout, and she saw the Gemini children running towards her, followed closely by a ram with sparkling horns.

"Hello Mother, we're back!" Brother called out as they ran up to her. "We met Aries and Taurus over the hill."

Cancer Mother sighed inwardly and braced herself for the cheerful onslaught.

"Look at Aries' horns!" said Brother, "Is Baby asleep?"

"Aries hurt his foot," Sister told her, "can you make it better?"

Aries and Gemini Sister started pushing close to Mother, trying to get a look at her closely protected Baby. At last, Cancer Baby woke up and smiled at them.

"We didn't wake him, did we?" said Aries.

Mother looked at Aries properly for the first time.

"Have you hurt your foot, then?" she asked with concern. "There, there! Let me make it better with a kiss."

Aries backed off hurriedly. "No kiss, thank you! It doesn't hurt now anyway."

As the ram didn't want her caring, Mother turned her attention back to Baby who was starting to fuss. She held him closer to her breast to feed, and he began sucking noisily. A warm smile spread over her face – Cancer Mother and Baby had become again a single loving life, each fulfilling the needs of the other.

Brother rolled his eyes, amazed that anyone could be so uninterested in their surroundings. The Gemini twins nudged the ram to go with them, and the three quietly crept away.

Once they were out of her earshot, they began to discuss Cancer, trying to understand.

"Mother never puts Baby down," said Brother, imagining feeling trapped in those arms, "she says he will grow up to be more confidant if she is always there for him."

Sister sighed, "That must be nice for Baby."

"Rubbish," said Brother, "How can he ever grow up if he never puts his feet on the ground!"

Aries puzzled over it for a while with his head on one side, then suddenly reached his conclusion.

"A great beginning!" he said decisively. Brushing the situation from his mind, he lifted his head and looked all round sniffing the air. Something seemed to be calling him away but he had no idea what it could be. The ram felt stuck just standing about talking with these children, but he didn't know how to leave. All at once he chose his direction and, without a word of explanation to the twins, he dashed off.

"Where are you going now?" called Brother, sad to be losing such an interesting companion.

"To see what's over the next hill." The last words floated back to them on the breeze, for Aries was gone.

The twins looked at each other, adjusting to being just two again. Sister took Brother's hand and began to tell him how they didn't need anyone else really. But as they walked on together through the meadow, both were quietly hoping they would meet someone new. Nature smiled to herself as she listened, and arranged another meeting for them along their way.

Back by the stream, Cancer was relieved to see Aries and Gemini move away. Mother gazed down into Baby's face with such love for the life in her arms that she felt her heart would burst. Baby gazed back at her fond face. This sweet smile, these loving eyes – he felt his Mother must be the whole world!

Mother and Baby were so rapt in each other, that they didn't notice the approach of a lion who had come to the stream to drink. The lion had not noticed them either, because he had just woken from a magnificent dream. He had been dreaming of the beginning of the world.

In his dream, the rays of the rising sun had shone on his lion face alone. He had received its light into himself until his great mane radiated like another sun. Then, as he turned his face to the world around him, everything he gazed at burst into the light of day – he was the sun himself! What a dream!

When the lion woke up and really looked around,
he still felt that he had created the day, and he smiled
up at the sun as a colleague in the work of creation. He
strolled down to the stream to drink (creating worlds
is thirsty work!) and when he bent his head over the
water, he saw the most beautiful face shining up at him.
A huge golden mane was glowing in the sunlight like a
halo round the noble face. His heart was so moved that
he put back his head and roared his presence so that
Nature's world would know him. Then he drank deeply,
feeling good after a job well done.

He was disturbed in his drinking by the sound of a baby crying and, looking round, he saw Cancer there.

"Why is your baby making that noise?" he demanded, "I can hardly think!"

Mother had been clutching Baby tightly to protect him from danger and now she glared at the lion with a mixture of alarm and anger.

"You terrified him with that dreadful roaring," she complained indignantly – she too could be fierce. "Don't you dare come any nearer! You're not going to harm my Baby."

The lion looked surprised: how could anyone think that he had meant to frighten them, let alone hurt them! Yet here was this Mother glaring at him as though he had done something wrong. For a moment he felt quite crestfallen. The light died from his mane and his eyes became quite sad. He decided to leave this scene of such disappointment, and turned away.

When Baby saw the lion, he gurgled with pleasure. The roar had been a shock, but he felt safe again now, snuggling in Mother's arms. Now, as the lion turned to walk away, Baby struggled to reach out to him.

"Lion!" called Mother quickly, " You don't have to go. I'm sorry if I upset you."

The lion turned his great head with a loud sigh, and then he saw Baby's smile. He stopped still and his mane flickered back into life. Baby laughed with delight. The lion's heart swelled in his chest and, with softened eyes, he moved nearer to meet this tiny source of such wonderful sound. Shaking the golden fur round his head, he seemed to grow to twice the size. Very gently he put his great face close to Baby. Mother watched anxiously as Baby caught a handful of fur and tugged, but she need not have worried. The happy smile on Baby's face disarmed the great lion completely, and he only winced.

"My name is Leo, little friend," he purred, his voice as soft and friendly as he could make it (but still a bit too loud). "When you are bigger, you may ride on my back."

Mother felt delighted by this offer, imagining her prince of a baby in control of a golden lion, and the three spent a while chatting and playing together. They were so engrossed in their new friendship that none of them noticed a tall, gentle figure walking towards them.

Chapter Three

Virgo approached the group with quiet modesty. She had been inspecting this new world, holding her skirt carefully off the grass and soil. She felt strongly that she should know more about the plants than she actually did. In her sleep she had heard soft whispering, as though Nature had been speaking to her, and now she couldn't remember anything that was said. So she was looking carefully at everything that surrounded her, to try to recall the instructions. The trees bent their growing branches happily to her gentle inquiry and the flowers smiled up at her, but she was too worried to notice their subtle responses.

Then she caught sight of a mother and baby with a lion, and she gratefully accepted the distraction from her study of Nature. 'Who are these?' she wondered to herself as she approached, while they looked questioningly at her troubled face.

"What's the matter, dear?" asked Mother.

"Hello, I'm Leo!" announced Leo proudly.

Baby gurgled.

Virgo studied them carefully, one at a time. "My name is Virgo," she said shyly, "Can I help you?"

"We're fine now that Leo has stopped roaring,"
Mother reassured her, then asked, "You look worried,
dear, is anything the matter?"

Virgo didn't think of herself. "I'm just concerned
about that gurgling," she said, "it sounds a bit odd. Is
your baby alright?"

Mother, immediately anxious, began checking her
happy child.

Virgo turned to Leo. "Your mane is a bit tangled, can
I help you smooth it out?" she offered.

Leo's brilliance dimmed as he thought of looking
tangled, then brightened again at the thought of having
someone to tend to him, even if she was a bit on the
serious side. After all, Cancer's attention had withdrawn
from him as Mother and Baby were once more involved
with each other.

Leo turned to Virgo. "My mane is fine as it is," he
said loftily, "but you may accompany me in a walk along
the stream, if you like." Cancer certainly seemed to have
forgotten they were there, so Virgo rested a gentle hand
on Leo's shoulder, and they walked slowly away.

They strolled upstream along a winding path,
Leo telling her about his dream and Virgo listening
attentively. All about them in the meadow they could
feel the ground adjusting under their feet as Nature
grew ferns and bushes in the grass, and stretched the
roots of saplings, encouraging them into little trees.

They reached a place where the little stream flowed
out of newly forming woods, and there they stopped
in surprise. On the grassy bank in front of them, sat a
lovely person leaning back elegantly, propped on one
hand. Her head drooped slightly to one side as she
gazed sadly into the flowing water. She looked up at
their approach, her eyes widening in relief.

"Thank goodness, there's someone else here," the
gentle voice spoke through an appealing smile. "What's
the good of all this beauty, if there's no-one to share it?"

"Don't worry," said Virgo, "there's Leo and me here,
and a mother and baby as well, back there in the
meadow."

"How nice for them to have each other," the sweet
smile was a little wistful. "And you are two together."

Leo was admiring the person's grace and style.
"We're not really 'together', you know," he said, "Would
you care to join me?"

Virgo looked from one to the other, now feeling that
her usefulness lay in another direction. "I – er – think I'll
get on with my work," she said, "there is so much I need
to know about all this growth."

She turned her attention once more to the plants

that were growing around them in ever greater profusion. "There's so much to do!" she added, bending down. Virgo had noticed a vine twining its way round a delicate flower, so she separated them and twisted the vine up a little tree trunk instead. Nature was delighted. "Thank you," she breathed, and the hem of Virgo's skirt moved a little in the breeze.

The lady by the stream gracefully stood up and rested a hand on Leo's now glowing mane.

"See you later," she said to Virgo over her shoulder, while Leo had forgotten about Virgo already. And so they walked contentedly together along the path into the woods.

"My name is Libra, I think," the person's voice spoke softly, "I am so pleased to meet you. Your mane is the most beautiful golden colour – surely it shines brighter than the sun!"

Leo grew larger at every word of the compliment until he was in danger of pushing Libra off the path. He mellowed his voice as best he could to match Libra's musical tones.

"I have never seen such grace as yours, Libra," he said to her, "you truly are a worthy companion for me." Leo felt his heart swelling in his chest. He took a deep breath. "Let us be friends for ever!" he cried with a passion that shook his mane, leaving a trail of golden dust on the path behind them.

Chapter Four

Libra and the lion walked into the woods, Leo
hardly noticing where his feet were taking them.
Gradually the woods were becoming denser and the
trees bigger, so that there was no longer much light on
the path, but Leo and Libra were too engrossed in each
other to notice. They were finally distracted from their
mutual admiration by a low growling noise. It sounded
at first far off, then very close, and eventually it seemed
to have its source behind them, cutting off their retreat.

"What's that noise?" Libra clutched Leo's fading
mane with growing anxiety.

"Never fear!" said Leo, trying to puff himself up,
"I'll take care of you!" But he had actually shrunk to his
smallest size yet.

"Perhaps we shouldn't be here," suggested Libra, "maybe we've disturbed someone else's place."

The growling continued to circle them and they looked this way and that to see what was making it, each trying to hide behind the other.

"You do the talking," Leo quavered, "you put things so nicely, whatever 'it' is won't hurt you." Then he added quickly, "If it notices how strong and fierce I am, it's bound to attack us!" Although this seems shameful behaviour for a lion, it was in fact very sensible considering the circumstances. Libra was not impressed, however. She would have run away if Leo had not been behind her and the growling now in front.

"We come in peace!" Libra called out, not knowing exactly where to look, and she gave the most disarming smile she could.

The growling stopped, and out of the dimness of the forest leaves lumbered a large, powerful creature. Libra and Leo were shocked into silence at the sight.

The creature stood on its hind legs, which were short and sturdy. Its huge chest seemed to be armour-plated. Even as they watched, other pieces of armour seemed to be dropping away from its body, exposing its coarse shaggy hair. Then a metallic tail with a stinger on the end suddenly fell off with a clatter. The head was waving from side to side, and the brows were so big, and frowning so ferociously, that its eyes could hardly be seen. Sharp teeth showed as it spoke for the first time, voice husky and slow.

"What do you want in my forest?" it demanded angrily.

"We were admiring your beautiful stream," Libra answered quickly, "It's amazing how far one can walk without noticing, when the surroundings are so lovely – isn't it?"

As the creature made no immediate move, Libra's confidence grew, and her smile became more genuine and, consequently, more appealing.

The creature shuffled about on the path, dropping more bits of its armour while making moves to sit down. Its frown was still in place but its teeth had disappeared somewhere in the hair of its face.

"Well," began Leo edging backwards, "I – er – I think we will be getting back now. Cancer will be wondering where we've gone."

The teeth reappeared and the creature's rumbling threatened to become a growl, as if it now didn't want them to go. So Leo stopped moving and wondered what would happen next.

Libra was intrigued that the creature seemed to want them to stay. He was sitting down looking from one to the other of them, no longer belligerent but curious. Now that his brows were relaxing, his eyes appeared. They were large, yellowy-greeny-brown, like pebbles under water, and the creature seemed to be looking through them from somewhere deep inside his being.

Slowly he spoke again. "I thought I was the only one in the world", he said, "I was safe inside my armour, with poison in the tail. Then you pushed in and I thought I'd get rid of you. But, when I thought of you leaving, this hair started growing and pushing my armour off – that made me growl."

"You're still safe," said Libra happily, "we wouldn't want to hurt you – perhaps we could be friends. Or would you rather be alone?"

The big eyes became rounder and full of water. "Actually, I was just beginning to feel lonely," one tear dropped onto the creature's chest, landing on his last piece of armour and dissolving it. "I hope I didn't frighten you too much." Another tear dropped and splashed onto the ground at his feet.

Libra and Leo were so moved by his tears, they walked up close to him, and he reached out his hands to them both.

"You really are so soft and sensitive," said Libra taking his hand.

"How gently you stroke my mane!" exclaimed Leo.

And the creature wept quietly.

"I will call you Scorpio," decided Libra, after some deliberation, "in memory of the armour you let go. But you must promise not to growl too loudly, and you must keep your teeth hidden. We need to be nice to each other for this lovely place to remain so peaceful and beautiful."

Leo, beginning to grow larger again, was nodding in agreement all through this speech.

But Scorpio began to frown again. "I will do what I feel like doing," he said forcefully, "If I behaved like you, I would not be me!"

Leo carried on nodding, because it had just occurred to him that being gentle like Libra might be a bit tame. 'How can I raise the morning sun if I may not shake my mane and roar?' he thought. 'Libra may be very pleasant company, but this is going a bit too far.'

"Well – I guess we are all different," admitted Libra, "but please, don't harm anyone."

Leo and Scorpio looked at Libra's kind face, appreciating the earnestness in her gentle eyes, and their three hearts joined in agreement.

Leo, Libra and Scorpio began walking back along the stream, and all the way they were talking together, getting to know each other better. They didn't notice all around them how Nature was growing the wood older and more spacious. They were so engrossed in conversation that neither did they notice the gradual changing of Scorpio's body.

His face was narrowing so that his large deep eyes were nearer the sides of his head. Where his teeth had been, a beak protruded. The shaggy hair had diminished, finally becoming soft smooth feathers over his head, his back and rounded chest. His hands, which he had clasped behind him as they walked, could no longer be seen, and a closed fan of splendid tail feathers had appeared. Only the sturdy legs remained the same, and even they were growing large claws instead of toes.

At last the group came out of the tree-green dimness by the place where Libra had been found that morning. The warm sun shone over the meadow, now quite overgrown with bushes. Large outcrops of rock were pushing heavily up out of the ground, grinding and crumbling where there was not enough space for them. The three friends watched in surprise feeling the deep rumbling sounds vibrating the earth beneath them. Then Leo and Libra turned their surprise to Scorpio, whose new body was now obvious in the light.

"Scorpio!" cried Leo, "What have you been doing!"

"I don't know what you mean," said Scorpio a bit huffily, shaking his shoulders to adjust the eagle wings that had replaced his arms. "But I do feel much more myself."

Libra's head tilted on one side then the other while she considered the new appearance of their friend from every angle. She felt somehow more respectful of the Scorpio eagle than she had done of the fierce monster he had seemed before.

"You look more confident now." Libra's respect was tinged with admiration. "I like it!"

Chapter Five

Leo, the lion, and the elegant Libra were just
beginning to get used to their friend, Scorpio, as an
eagle, when suddenly their thoughts were scattered by
a sharp hiss and thump, as a burning arrow stuck in the
ground a bit too near for comfort.

There followed a shout, a thundering of hooves,
and a swirl of noise, wind and dust, as a small centaur
stamped into the group. A man's head and body
extended from the neck of a horse body. He was
wielding a bow in one hand, and a quiver of arrows was
slung round his waist. He looked from one to the other
of them while constantly moving about. The horse-half
kept walking in a different direction from that faced by

the man-half, so he had to keep twisting and turning to hold his focus steady on any one in the group. The three watching him became quite confused by the result.

At last, the centaur reached down and plucked the arrow out of the ground. Blowing out the flame, he pushed it expertly back into his quiver with the others.

"I wondered where that arrow would land!" he shouted, shaking his brown curly hair. "And it brought me to you! There had to be someone else in this world, it stands to reason!"

"What reason?" asked Scorpio coldly, trying to fix the centaur with his eagle eye.

"You know – a place like this, so full of possibilities," the centaur waved his arms about expansively. "Anyway, here we are! Any idea how big 'it' all is?"

There was a soft rustling roundabout the little group as a gentle breeze lifted the centaur's brown curls. They all realized that the rustling was whispering words: *"It's all inside."*

"Who said that?" Leo was startled.

"I don't know," said the centaur, "It happens whenever I ask a question, and I don't understand the answers half the time."

"Do you mean to say," said Scorpio, "that someone answers all your questions and you haven't figured out who it is yet!"

"Well, I can't see anyone, can you?"

They all looked around but didn't see anyone, and neither did they notice, floating a little way above the centaur's head, two large eyes full of stars twinkling at them. The eyes were similar to the centaur's own eyes, but larger, and they were almost invisible.

Libra was thinking how much easier life would be if decisions were made by 'someone who knows' instead of trying to guess what would be best. After all, she thought, to make a decision properly, one really needs to know everything about it. So she decided to ask a question herself.

"Ask what we ought to do next!" she said eagerly.

The centaur looked back a bit scathingly. He thought that 'finding out' was much more fun than 'being told', but he asked Libra's question anyway, and the rustling whisper came back: "Your choice."

Libra frowned with disappointment, a strange expression for her smooth features. It was an anxious burden trying to keep the peace, not rock the boat, create endless harmony and perfect balance. The answer 'Your choice' had just placed that burden again on the delicate Libran shoulders, and it weighed on her heavily.

"Well, it's not much help, is it!" she said, with an elegant shrug, and moved away from the others. Libra sat once again where Leo and Virgo had found her, on the grassy bank of the stream, and crossly tried not to cry.

"No spirit of adventure, if you ask me," said the centaur, and no one pointed out that they hadn't asked him at all.

"By the way, you guys, I call myself Sagittarius," the centaur looked at Leo and Scorpio, forgetting to ask their names. "What do you say we explore downstream a bit? I'm longing to see where this stream actually goes!"

"I'm busy," said Scorpio curtly. His feathers were definitely beginning to get a little ruffled. He began to straighten them, burying his sharp beak in their softness, which fortunately muffled his other comments – "hair-brained schemes", "lot of nonsense" and "more important things to do".

Leo was considering what 'exploring downstream' might be like with Sagittarius, and he managed to look expectant and apprehensive at the same time, his mane glittering and his size uncertain.

"Come on then!" said Sagittarius, not waiting for an answer but galloping off along the stream towards the woods.

Before Leo had time to follow, the centaur realized that he was going upstream by mistake, stopped, turned his man-body one way, his horse-body the other, and nearly fell over his own hooves. Leo was delighted at the spectacle and roared with laughter.

Getting himself sorted out at last, Sagittarius waved his bow and was off downstream with Leo happily bounding along behind. Had they looked up, they would have seen the two knowing eyes within that whispering presence floating above them. The Mind of Oneness watched them as they went, but neither of them noticed. Greater understanding always travelled with Sagittarius because he was looking for it.

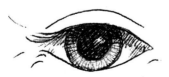 

Chapter Six

Sagittarius constantly looked this way and that, taking in the changing scenery and throwing comments to Leo over his shoulder. "Look at that hill!" "I wonder what's over there." "I don't remember seeing rocks like that before." And so on.

They crossed the meadow by a path where the grass was still short and, rounding a bend in the stream, they heard a soft gentle singing, and saw Mother rocking her Baby to the rhythm of Nature's heart beat.

"Home!" whispered the breeze.

Sagittarius stood open-mouthed and still for a moment. There was a swelling feeling in his heart, which was unfamiliar, and it disturbed him strangely.

"Hello, Cancer!" called Leo, and trotted over to tell Mother all about his adventures. He was torn between, on one hand wanting to introduce his newfound friend, the centaur, and, on the other hand not wanting to share his audience. But thinking about it he realised that bringing Sagittarius over to Cancer would enlarge the audience, which wouldn't be a bad thing. So, with a flourish, he included the centaur who was approaching slowly, tentatively.

"And THIS is Sagittarius, isn't he amazing!"

"Hello, dear," Mother said, looking at this new creature and smiling at him. Then her eyes filled with tears because she could see the gentle, knowing eyes regarding her from the air above him, and at once she felt the centaur's bewilderment. 'How sad,' she thought, 'that he is so close to the understanding that he wants so much, and yet can't quite make the connection.' Kindly, she held Baby towards him.

"This is my Baby," she said, "I hope you will teach him some day."

"Oh!" gasped the centaur, "Well, I – I –" He looked over his shoulder for inspiration and turned round a few times, but for once the breeze was silent. Sagittarius would have loved to say 'Yes, of course!' but he didn't know what he would teach. He felt only how much he wanted to learn, and all that he had learned so far seemed so obvious to him that he supposed everybody must know those things!

"Right!" he said, "OK!" This confusion of emotions was too much for him, so at last he called out "I'll see you later!" and galloped away downstream.

Leo didn't understand all this, and watched him go with amazement.

"How odd!" he shrugged, "Anyway, Cancer, you'd LOVE this elegant Libra person that I met. And Scorpio! Well, it's difficult to say if he's a beast or a bird!"

Cancer Mother felt more concerned about those characters she had met, so she asked Leo, "Have you seen Aries? He hurt his foot, you know." Then she told Leo about Aries' wonderful sparkly horns, and Leo began to feel more interested in continuing his journey than listening to Cancer going on about someone else's splendour.

"Sounds wonderful," he said half-heartedly, gazing after his centaur friend. "I wonder what Sagittarius is up to?" And he bounded off, calling back, "Have fun!"

All through the meadow, Nature had been carving grooves in the earth so that the stream gathered little tributaries as it went. Gradually it opened out into a fair sized river flowing gently beside the adventuring pair. Leo and Sagittarius slowed to a walk. They had left Cancer in her meadow and were now in territory Leo had not seen before. The smell of warm earth, and the lush green grass, scattered with the colours of many little flowers, soothed the friends and they chatted about the creatures they had seen so far.

Suddenly the centaur stopped, pointing his bow at an earthy brown mound of animal ahead of them that neither of them had met before.

"Hey! What's that?" he cried.

The mound raised a large head and gazed at
them, and they could see clearly now that it was a
cow. Enormous brown eyes were fringed with long
dark lashes. It was Taurus, still sitting where Aries
and Gemini had left her. When she saw a lion and a
centaur approaching her with such energy, she paused
uncertainly in her munching, and looked round for
some solid support.

"Hello!" said Sagittarius, "what's going on here?"

Now they were closer, they could also see a goaty
creature sitting behind the cow. Only its head showed

behind Taurus's large body, and it was looking decidedly away from them all.

"Well, hello," said Taurus slowly, "Gemini says my name is Taurus. Who are you?"

"Oh yes!" the centaur laughed and introduced them. "I'm Sagittarius, and this is Leo. We're exploring to see where this stream goes."

"What stream? It looks like a river to me." said Taurus.

"So it is!" cried Sagittarius, looking at it again. "It was a stream where we came from. I never noticed how big it was growing!" Then: "What have you been learning, Taurus?"

Taurus was encouraged by the centaur's easy warmth, and began to tell him about her experience.

"Sitting here is so peaceful. I smell the flowers and feel the gentle breeze. Capricorn is here now, and he tells me how useful it is being 'earthy.' We both really feel the earth, you see," she said softly, smiling down at it. "Capricorn, will you explain to them?"

The sharp horns and pointy face turned towards them at last as the goaty creature began to get up reluctantly from behind the comfortable cow. Cautiously he straightened thin, knobbly front legs and stood on his cloven hoofs. His legs stepped forward awkwardly, as though dragging behind them a weight that was still hidden. Taurus looked round at Capricorn and pushed at him gently with her large, soft nose, encouraging his full emergence into the gaze of Leo and Sagittarius.

"I can manage perfectly well!" Capricorn spoke defensively, as he pulled a large fishtail into view. Leo was shocked almost speechless.

"Don't say anything!" hissed the lion at his friend but, after a slight pause, Sagittarius could not hold back his wonder.

"What an amazing tail!" he shouted, and Leo winced as he added, "and only two legs! You're like a sort of mermaid, no – a mer-goat!"

The eyes above Sagittarius looked gently at Capricorn, while the breeze whispered to them all: "*His is the ancient wisdom of the sea.*"

Capricorn heard the whispered words of understanding and stood more confidently.

"I know how things are meant to go," he said, "but you have to be careful, look at the pros and cons, weigh things up, and so on. If you go rushing off, like that Aries-thing we saw flashing past a while ago, you won't know where you are going or what to do when you get there!"

Leo hadn't been listening. "Doesn't it get in the way?" he asked, waving a paw towards the fishtail. "I mean, if you were in the sea it would be useful – but on land?"

"I keep my tail behind me," said Capricorn loftily, "If I ignore all that watery, emotional stuff and focus on what I am doing, you'd be surprised how much I can achieve."

"Now, Capricorn," said Sagittarius, "what were you telling Taurus about being 'earthy'? Can anyone be earthy? Is it a good idea?"

Capricorn took a deep breath while he thought how to answer these questions.

"Well, you see," he said eventually, "our bodies are all made of this earth, like the trees and the hills and, if we want our bodies to work well, we should eat what they need, and exercise them properly. Then we can do what needs to be done. That's being earthy!"

"Capricorn tells me," Taurus added quietly, "that people feel safe and well when they are with me."

"How does that work?" Sagittarius was getting really interested now.

"I love Nature, and Nature loves me." She breathed lovingly on the flowers, and they smiled back at her. "I know I'm safe, so everyone near me can just relax and enjoy being alive." She looked inquiringly at Capricorn, and finished a bit lamely, "Well, something like that."

They all nodded wisely, although Leo looked a bit sceptical.

Suddenly, not far away, a lot more rocks began pushing up through the ground, and everything seemed to move. The ground beneath them heaved, rocked and shifted, and they all staggered a bit. Leo, without thinking, found himself moving closer to Taurus, and she smiled.

"That's right," she said soothingly, "come and sit down with me. Nature is just moving into a more comfortable position," she reassured them, "she's new like us, you know, and being alive takes getting used to. Besides she's busy growing all this scenery, and something has to move to make room."

So they all settled down around Taurus and tried to feel the safety of Nature's love.

Chapter Seven

Scorpio stood on his own. He hadn't wanted to dash off with Sagittarius, the centaur, as Leo had done. Just now he wasn't interested to find out where the stream was going – he was more interested in discovering what this new body could and couldn't do. Although Libra was now sleeping gracefully on the grass, Scorpio walked a little way along the stream until he was sure no one could see him. Now at last, he could begin to investigate what had happened to him.

He had definitely become an eagle. The eagle body was so much better than that first cold armour he wore, to protect himself in the woods. It was also much better than being the lonely monster that Leo and Libra had met when the armour dropped off.

Scorpio felt good being an eagle, but he wasn't sure exactly what an eagle could do. He preened his wing feathers for a while, and then looked round once more to make sure no one was watching. Gently he began to stretch out one of his wings. He could feel the joints opening strangely as he continued to stretch. Then all at once the momentum of the movement took over and a ripple of energy extended his wing to the end of its feathers, separating them and lifting them up at the tips.

He folded the wing in again, and then tried stretching out both wings at the same time. At their fullest extension, something in his big chest seemed to open and, in a burst of exuberance, he flapped the wings with all his strength. They hit the ground, stirring up clouds of dust, which caught in his throat and hurt his eyes.

"Oh well," muttered Scorpio, folding both wings on his back once more, "It was nice while it lasted." But the question about his wings didn't go away: 'I wonder what they're for?' he thought.

For want of anything better to do, Scorpio decided to follow the lion and centaur downstream. He stomped along through newly sprouting bushes and ferns, marvelling at the piles of rock that seemed to be only just settling into place. Grass was growing quickly over them wherever it could find a crack to push in roots. He had not seen this part of the world before and wondered if the ground was always this unsteady.

The stream was growing much bigger as other little streams flowed in, and he was just wondering how far Leo and Sagittarius had explored along it, when he saw Cancer ahead of him, sitting on one of the grassy rocks. Mother and Baby were playing a game that set Baby giggling, and Scorpio watched them for a while. He was reluctant to go forward and meet them because he felt safer on his own.

At last Mother looked up and saw the eagle standing

there, a distance away. She could feel how much he needed loving, and her heart went out to him. The look of tenderness in her eyes reached him across the distance, and with tears welling up in his own eyes he stomped towards her. Baby was a bit frightened of the sharp beak, and clung tightly to Mother.

"It's alright, my little One," she reassured Baby, "we are all babies inside. We all need to love and be loved so we can feel good." And to the eagle she added, "Isn't that right? You need to be loved, too!"

"That's right, we all need love." Scorpio's deep voice was husky with emotion and, to distract her from himself, he added, "and don't forget, you need to be loved as much as your baby."

Cancer Mother looked at him, puzzled for a moment, and then sighed.

"I know my baby loves me," she said, "but, yes, you're right. It isn't fair to balance my love for Baby with Baby's love for me. After all he is so very tiny and needs to concentrate on loving himself so he can grow. Tell me, Scorpio, where is the love I need?"

Scorpio shook his wings a bit, and sorted out a few feathers with his beak to hide his uncertainty. "Why don't we follow the river together," he said. "Perhaps we shall find Love on the way."

All this time, Libra had been sleeping on the grass near the woods. She had been so hopeful that Sagittarius' wise voice would answer her questions. When she asked what she should do next, and the voice had answered 'Your choice', Libra had been so disappointed. She felt suddenly challenged in the deepest, most fearful place inside.

'Supposing I choose something that spoils things!' Libra thought, and anxiety went round and round in her beautiful head. She had withdrawn from the rest of the group to try and solve the problem, and finally fell asleep. There she slept while Leo and Sagittarius went off exploring downstream, followed later by Scorpio. Still she slept while Nature grew a beautiful garden of flowers around her.

At last, out of the undergrowth, rushed the Gemini twins, a whirl of arms and legs, but hand in hand as usual. They both stopped at once as they saw the sleeping lady surrounded by beautiful flowers.

"Wow!" Brother exclaimed, waking her with the sound. He stared with his mouth open as she sat up and stretched. No words came to express the feeling in his heart.

"You're very beautiful," said Sister shyly, "who are you?"

Libra smiled at the two children, charmed by their innocence and their companionship with each other.

"My name is Libra," she said, extending both hands to them. Brother and Sister each took hold of a hand and pulled, to help Libra stand up, but the ground was wobbling so that they all tumbled together, laughing with pleasure at each other. At last they could stand, and naturally walked together along the path by the stream, following the paw-prints of lion, hoof-prints of centaur and claw-prints of eagle that showed the way. As they went, the trees listened to their happy chatter, and flowers glowed brighter as laughter scattered happiness through the air.

Gemini and Libra ran and skipped along beside the growing stream. After a while they caught up with Cancer Mother cradling Baby in her arms as she walked steadily along with the great eagle, Scorpio.

"Hallo, Cancer!" shouted Brother as they passed, "Who's your friend?"

"Don't run too fast!" warned Mother. "Have you seen Aries?"

Brother didn't reply because he, Sister and Libra were already around the next bend in the river, the three skipping on happily.

That was when the ground really heaved, and it sent them sprawling. Brother and Sister were up first, looking all round to see where the movement had come from, and wondering whether to cry or not. Libra stood up carefully and then reached out to hold the twins close. She brushed them down and smoothed their hair.

"Don't worry," Libra's gentle voice reassured them and herself, "I'm sure everything's alright really. Let's carry on along the path – perhaps we'll find someone who knows what's going on."

At last, in the distance, they saw a group of five creatures sitting on the grass. Libra recognized Leo and Sagittarius sitting on the ground close beside the reclining body of a cow. Gemini both recognized the cow as Taurus still sitting where they had left her ages before. But Capricorn, propped up on his goaty front legs with his fishtail tucked behind him, was a new and amazing sight to them all, and careful Virgo had also joined the group, still searching for knowledge.

Virgo had been sharing with them all something she had discovered about the plants. It seemed that everything was vibrating at slightly different rates, and every rate made a different colour, which was why all the flowers were different colours. Taurus, who had been munching on all the flowers she could reach, realised that she had been feeling different with each colour she ate.

"Blue Speedwell is peaceful," Taurus murmured to herself, "and red Poppy is lively, and these yellow Celandines make me feel so happy!"

Sagittarius was so fascinated that he, too, kept eating different flowers, trying out the idea to see if it worked. As Gemini and Libra joined them, Sagittarius was excitedly telling them all that the colours could change their mood.

"So that means," he concluded, "you just eat the colour that vibrates the mood you want to have!"

Leo was getting a bit bored, his mane lank and dull, and Capricorn was wondering whether Nature would start shaking the ground again, and if so what would be the safest thing to do.

Leo was delighted to see Libra and Gemini coming towards them.

"Right!" he said, jumping up decisively, "Now that you're here, we can all make a move!"

Gradually the whole party clambered to their feet, including Taurus. She had never stood before and kept her face very near the ground, feeling she would be more secure that way. Brother ran round her legs laughing.

"Wow! She's got legs!" he shouted, "Hey, Taurus! Catch me!" He tugged Sister by the hand, so they could chase along the river, but Sister was smiling at Taurus, and stroking the cow's smooth brown hide.

"Come on!" Brother urged his Sister and, laughing together, the twins ran off in front.

"Come!" said Leo regally, when they were all standing at last, and he walked after the children. With beautiful Libra's hand resting again on his golden mane, he didn't think about where they were actually going.

Virgo made helpful noises to Taurus, "There," and "That's right," helping her to feel that standing was natural and safe.

Capricorn looked up at the sky and around at the horizon for signs to indicate the best course of action. In several places, he noticed, the river banks had overflowed, soaking the ground. 'It would be better for us all to stay together,' he thought. He felt that the others should have waited to choose a safer path, but as they had gone, Capricorn decided to add his moral support to Taurus. So the three moved away at a slow and dignified pace, leaving Sagittarius gazing into space.

The breeze had begun to whisper to Sagittarius again. The centaur stood still for a while, cocking his head to hear better what he was being told. It seemed there was to be a great happening, and a place of gathering for all creatures, but he couldn't be sure what the happening would be, nor where to gather. He shook his head, bringing himself back to the world of action, and galloped after the others.

Cancer and the eagle Scorpio, were approaching at a leisurely pace. They too had been shaken by the sudden tremors of Nature's growth, and Cancer had fallen over. Scorpio carefully helped Mother to her feet, and they discovered with relief that Baby was unharmed, being closely protected from the ground by Mother's arms. They continued their hopeful quest for Love.

Ahead in the distance, they could just see the earthy trio, of Taurus with Virgo and Capricorn on either side, making its slow way along the river. There was only a cloud of spray to show where the centaur's hooves had galloped across the flooded ground. Mother and Scorpio looked at each other without speaking. They each felt the other's growing excitement, and followed the rest of the creatures full of great hope.

Chapter Eight

All this time, far up in the highest mountain, a young man with light blue eyes had been watching the comings and goings of these strange creatures far below. From down there, the mountain looked like a cloud in its misty distance and they knew nothing of his presence.

So far the man had felt only mildly interested in these creatures because they were a very small part of all that he could see: there were forests and meadows, rivers and hills, all changing and growing. While above it all rested the deep blue sky with a brilliant sun. He could see with his mind, even beyond the blue to the stars sprinkling their patterns in the dark. Sometimes a breeze would blow, whispering wordlessly in his ears, and at those times he felt as though someone 'out there' was watching him.

Every time Nature created something big in the world below him, he felt tremors through the rocks, but he seemed to be safe enough. Then there was a deep rumbling from inside the mountain, growing louder and louder. At first he was unaware that it had anything to do with him, but then the rocks where he sat shook with the force of the sound. He gazed about for some understanding to hold onto, but at last was shaken from his seat and rolled a short way down the mountainside.

When the rocks were steady again, he looked down into the world and noticed that the river had slopped over its banks and flooded some of the land. The creatures below him had also been shaken about, and now they were gathering together and all setting off in the same direction.

He looked out in the direction they seemed to be taking, and saw something that he hadn't noticed before: a huge stretch of water that extended away from him into distances beyond knowing. The sea! It started down there somewhere at the edge of the land.

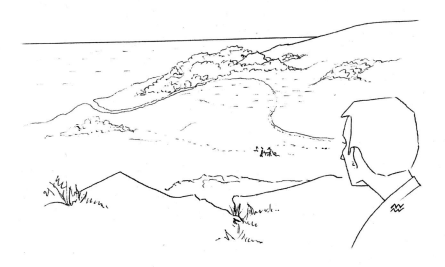

In fact the creatures appeared to be following the river that had overflowed its banks. The flood had created a swamp between those creatures and the sea. 'And if they continue along the river,' he thought, 'they will get themselves bogged down.'

He felt a strong reluctance to give up his bird's eye view, but it was finally overcome by an equally strong urge to sort out their route for them. So, he continued his descent down the mountainside by choice, making his way carefully over the loosened boulders.

The man was first spotted by Sagittarius, the centaur being at the front of the expedition by now, and looking around as he always did.

"Who are you?" Sagittarius called without stopping.

"Do you realize where you're going?" asked the man in reply. The centaur stopped.

"We're following the river to see where it goes," he answered brightly. "Would you like to come with us?"

"I don't need to come with you," the man had taken two steps back, and looked wistfully over his shoulder at the mountain of his sweet solitude.

"Please yourself," said Sagittarius with a smile, "It's your choice." And the breeze blew from the centaur towards the man, to remind the man of what he had come to tell them all.

The Gemini twins arrived, together with Leo the lion, and the lovely Libra.

"You are all going towards the sea," said the man, the light of his vision shining from his blue eyes. "You can follow the river if you like, but if you do you'll become lost in wetlands and stuck in a swamp."

"So what should we do?" asked Libra, falling instantly in love with those far-seeing eyes.

"If you will take this other path away from the river, closer to the mountain, you will get to the sea quicker and more safely."

"How do you know that?" asked Capricorn, just then catching up with them.

"He just knows!" cried Sagittarius, "You can tell by the light in his eyes, and I'm going the way he says." He waved his bow at the indicated path with such enthusiasm that the rest of the company felt it might be worth a try.

'It's alright for this newcomer,' thought Capricorn, 'He comes into the group from outside! No responsibility for anyone but himself! Tells the rest of us where to go! Where was he when the ground shook and frightened everyone!' Capricorn couldn't see the sense in leaving the river if you wanted to know where it was going, but he felt in his bones that the stranger was right. Although he would have liked more practical proof, he decided to trust his feelings and go with the rest. 'I knew there was something wrong with all that soggy ground,' he told himself.

"You must be Aquarius," said Capricorn out loud, not knowing quite how he knew the name, "coming down out of the blue like that. Perhaps you had better lead us as you have the gift of vision."

"You may call me Aquarius if you like," said the young man, "But I'm not leading. Vision may be useful, but someone else is needed to look out for people along the way – that's your gift, Capricorn. Do you know that every one of us has a gift to give the group? And all the gifts add up to a perfect way of living all together. Sometimes we need someone to cheer us up and inspire us when the going gets tough – that's Sagittarius's gift. So perhaps we had better follow him along that path!"

Virgo wanted to make sure that everyone was there, so that none should be left behind. She was so intent that her usual shyness was forgotten.

"Are we all here?" she called, checking them. "The Gemini twins, Libra, Leo and Sagittarius, and – " she stopped, dismayed, "Oh dear, how many are we supposed to be?"

No one was listening, but her fussing had given Taurus and Cancer time to catch up. Everyone gathered round Aquarius, and they set off along the better path to the sea, away from the soggy riverbanks.

As they travelled, they were intrigued about Aquarius' idea of having gifts to give that others might need. Aquarius had announced the gifts of Sagittarius and Capricorn; now each of the others wanted to hear what their special gift was.

"Aquarius," Libra asked at last, smiling sweetly into his fascinating blue eyes, "what do I have to give?"

"Your gift is to find the beauty of a middle way when people get into arguments. And the gift of these Gemini children running round us all, is lightening everyone's hearts."

Taurus had lumbered up close behind him and breathed warm air down his neck.

"Your gift," laughed Aquarius, rubbing her forehead then pushing her off, "is to bring comfort and healing to everyone. And Cancer's gift," he put an arm briefly round Mother's shoulders and smiled at Baby, "is to bring caring for the soul. Leo, now – he helps us feel important because he is so great that, when he glows at us, we feel great too! A wonderful gift!"

Leo grew a little bigger. He shook some golden dust from his mane, and decided not to mind Libra shifting her attention from himself to Aquarius.

"And Virgo," said Aquarius, looking into the earnest face, "your gift is to show them how to help each other."

Virgo smiled shyly, and reached out a hand to see if she could help Capricorn. 'He has taken on such an enormous job in looking out for the safety of us all,' she thought, 'perhaps some appreciation would help him.' She looked around at the rest of the group.

"We are all so different," she said, then she paused, looking back at the eagle. He was stomping awkwardly along behind them all, trying to look as though he hadn't heard and wouldn't be interested if he had.

"What about Scorpio?" asked Virgo, "what is his gift?"

"I'm not sure," said Aquarius, "perhaps we'll find out later on."

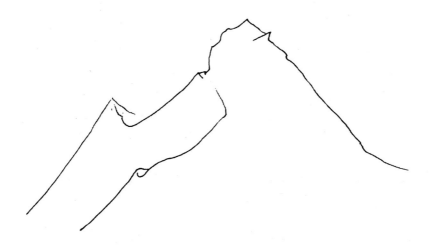

Chapter Nine

While they talked, the strange mix of creatures had been helping each other along the path, and they were now approaching a broad sandy beach with little waves lapping along it.

"It's the sea!" shouted the Gemini twins together, leaping up and clapping their hands.

"So this is where the river was going," muttered Capricorn to himself.

Then suddenly, up went a cry of "Aries!" for there was the ram. His legs were wet and sandy, his body was covered with mud and his curling horns were held high and brilliant.

"Oh, there you are, Gemini!" he called, "What a lot of friends you've found!"

Gemini Brother turned to Aquarius. "Aries's gift must be something about getting there first," he offered.

They all considered this, wondering how 'being first' could be good for others. Then Leo spoke up.

"It takes courage to follow your dreams," he told them with feeling, "I think his gift is the courage to be himself and go for what feels right to him. Very inspiring!" he added, lifting his Leonine head proudly.

"Well," said Aries, "I've been up and down this entire beach and I can't find a way round the water."

"There is no way round it!" Aquarius laughed, because from his mountain-top view it was obvious.

At that, they all began asking questions: "So what do we do now?" "Where do we go next?" "Is this a safe place to stop?" But no one could answer any of them.

Sagittarius thought back to the whispering voice and wondered if this was the time of the happening he had been told about.

Finally he said: "Well, we've found out where the river goes, and here we are together. Let's celebrate!"

Libra smiled round at the others. "We'll need a good place," she said, "somewhere we all feel happy."

Taurus walked around and finally chose a place on the beach that was not too near the waves and had the right feeling of security. There she sat down comfortably and munched, and the others gathered round.

"We should have a circle," stated Aquarius, "so that our place is clear."

"Yes, yes!" said Sagittarius, "and some of us could perform our gifts for the others."

Capricorn pulled his heavy fishtail across the sand, carefully marking out a circle close to where Taurus was sitting. Then he organised Virgo and the twins to remove the stones and seaweed so that the sand in the circle would be smooth.

"Isn't this pretty," said Sister, holding up a green feathery frond.

Brother admired it. "We could use this to decorate round the edge," he suggested, so he and Sister collected all they could find and arranged it prettily round the circle. With all their work, they soon felt tired and fell asleep against Taurus's warmth, holding hands as usual.

Cancer Mother, holding her sleeping Baby tenderly in her arms, sat down beside the cow and began to talk with Taurus about children and food and warmth and all the really important things in life. And a feeling of peace and comfort spread over the whole company.

Leo said that the sand might be a bit hard for sitting comfortably, and went with Libra and Aquarius back to the path. They brought armfuls of dry grass to the circle, and Scorpio arranged it round the edge with his beak.

Aries pranced around the group thinking of one good idea after another only to find that others had started doing it already. But his busy energy kept the workers going.

At last all felt ready. Brother and Sister awoke and quickly sat next to the circle. The others gathered round comfortably on the dry grass.

Leo walked dramatically round the circle scattering gold dust from his mane until the space felt festive and important. Finally he stood in the middle and opened the entertainment with a splendid roar.

When Leo had stepped out of the circle, there was a pause as everyone wondered what would happen next, and Aries just couldn't wait! He leapt into the circle and started the entertainment by telling how he had struggled along the river – through water and mud – on his own – and discovered the beach!

"I couldn't make out what all that water was, though," he laughed at himself, "and how did the rest of you manage to get here so clean and comfortable when I got in such a mess?"

Everyone laughed, and surprised Aries by clapping loudly. He quickly came out of the circle and sat down, almost embarrassed that they had actually been listening to him.

Then Sagittarius stepped his horse hooves delicately into the circle. Looking round at them all with his wild, excited eyes, he held his audience spellbound as they waited for him to begin. Only the splashing waves of the sea broke the silence.

"In the beginning, we were just stars in space," Sagittarius waved his arms towards the sky. "Our lovely world was only a dream."

Gradually Sagittarius unfolded the story of their creation, telling all their experiences from the beginning. Libra joined him in the circle and, while he spoke, she expressed in graceful movement all that he said. All the while, the centaur seemed to grow bigger. His eyes became deeper and his voice, although easily heard, sounded more like the whispering breeze.

When he spoke of each of the creatures and their part in the story, he would look at them, and they felt recognized and understood. At last, he concluded the story on this very beach. Libra twirled in a wonderful spiral and bowed to the ground, and everyone clapped and shouted their approval until they were quite hoarse.

Sagittarius took Libra's hand as they both left the circle. He was again a small centaur but the breeze blew round him, lifting his curly, brown hair, though it touched no one else at all.

Aquarius had been so enlightening on the journey, the others tried to get him to go into the circle but he shook his head and looked round at Scorpio. The eagle had withdrawn a little from the group and was now gazing up at the sky hoping intensely that no one would ask him to do anything.

So it looked as though the entertainment was over, when gradually they noticed that a wisp of spray from the sea had whirled its way towards them until it hovered in the centre of the circle.

"Pisces!" whispered Brother to Sister, but they couldn't see her very clearly because of all the tiny fishes swimming in the shaft of rainbow that surrounded her.

As they gazed, Pisces began to dance. She
shimmered into different colours, humming and
singing and laughing until her audience had forgotten
who they were and seemed to swim together with her
in a fairy world through the sea of changes. At last she

blew each one of them a kiss that gave them back their consciousness of themselves, and they gazed about in wonder. Pisces' gift was wonderful, but when they tried no one could put it into words!

Scorpio had been staring at Pisces' dance, knowing in his heart that something had changed for the whole group. He didn't know why but everything at last felt complete. In fact, they were now all twelve together, just as they had been when they were dot-to-dot pictures in the sky, before they were born into this little world.

Chapter Ten

Perhaps they were complete, all twelve creatures together at last, but Nature had not finished shaping her world for them. So far she had landscaped many different places, and grown many different plants and trees. The last huge upheaval had more clearly separated the land from the sea. Now the creatures were all together, but one more thing still remained to be done. Aquarius' mountain was too high. He would still be able to separate himself too far from the others, and she knew only one way to make it smaller. Nature focussed all her strength into the centre of the world and, with her life force, heated that centre into fire.

The world could not contain such force and was uncertain where to let it out. The sandy beach shuddered and lifted, the rocks heaved and shook.

All the creatures were tipped this way and that. They fell and rolled and tumbled over each other, with grunts and groans and cries, "Ouch!", "Sorry!", "What's happening!", "oh, Oh, OH!" All their differences faded in importance. They became a bunch of frightened creatures, trying not to be too hurt, or hurt each other in the confusion. At last the force broke through. The sky darkened with grey billowing clouds of dust lit with orange flames. Great booms of rolling thunder overpowered the sound of the sea, which was sloshing around like water in a bowl.

The ground stopped moving as suddenly as it had begun, but the air was still full of noise, and a confusion of light and cloud. Everyone rolled to a stop and lay where they were, gasping and feeling their bodies for damage – except Pisces. She had been floating a little off the ground all this time so that the movement had not affected her, and now she moved gently among the others, comforting and caring for them with a touch, a smile, a gentle look, healing with the love from her heart. Through her rainbow mist, they could see those wonderful eyes, which somehow looked familiar.

Aries jumped up. "I'm all right, I'm fine!" he shouted.

Sagittarius was not long in joining him. "That was fun!" he said, but his voice quavered a little. "I think it came from that cloud, or was it a mountain?"

"It was a mountain," confirmed Aquarius sadly, "I shall never again be able to sit so far above you all." He looked towards his old vantage point, now somewhat lower than it had been. "It's still spouting fire!" he cried in alarm.

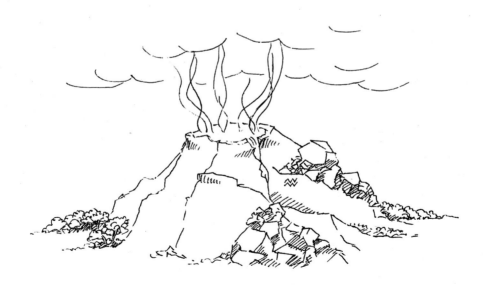

They all looked round at it feeling their fear renewed. It was Pisces who floated between them and the mountain, and then turned to face them all. She had landed on a large rock so that they could all see her where she stood. She waved her rainbow fins to quiet their questions, and light shone from her eyes.

"Don't be afraid, everyone," she said, her voice echoing the whispering breeze. "We are all here, all twelve of us. The number is complete, don't you see, and as long as we stay together, nothing can harm us."

They looked at her with amazement. Taurus was completely puzzled, and Gemini shook their heads at each other. But Sagittarius nodded – although he didn't quite understand yet, he knew she was right.

She continued: "We are just twelve different ways of expressing the Oneness that made us all. Oh dear, how can I say this?"

"I don't know," said Scorpio urgently, his feathers dusty but his eyes piercing and bright. "I don't know, but keep trying!"

"The Oneness has twelve faces, our faces, so when we look into each others eyes, we discover the Oneness that we really are!" Pisces' eyes glistened with tears as she felt how impossible it was for her to explain.

Cancer Mother gazed at her with a dawning light in her eyes. She leaned close to Scorpio. "Who we really are – Oneness – could that be the Love we were searching for?" she suggested.

Then Sagittarius leaped towards the rock, becoming larger as he landed. He stood beside Pisces, tall and wonderful. As he spoke, a great breeze blew the clouds of dust away. The fire in the mountain was gone, and their fear was fading.

"The most wonderful thing," he said, "is that there is nothing to fear, because everything is really One, and that Oneness loves everything. Pisces is telling us that each of us is also the Oneness, and that means we are that Love!"

For a moment everyone was still, feeling together and not separate. Looking round at each other, they blended into a speechless joyfulness. Their hearts filled with happiness until no one could contain the laughter, the tears, the simple physical energy. No one, that is, except Scorpio.

Suddenly they were all looking at the eagle. He was not moving, and seemed to be almost transparent. Because he had been able to stay still, he felt the light of his heart continue to expand with joy inside him, until it was shining out through his body.

"We ARE Love!" he said softly, "That was what I needed to know."

Gradually he spread out his great wings. The long feathers beat once slowly down and, with a sigh, he rose into the blue sky. All their hearts rose with him, as they realized that Scorpio was connecting them to that great Love – that was his gift!

Watching him disappear into the brilliance of the sun, they felt a peacefulness surrounding and filling them, beyond any understanding.

"Thank you," whispered Pisces, tears falling through her rainbow and over her feet, to join the sea.

At first they were all quiet, whispering to each other how wonderful everything was. Gradually they talked of

more ordinary things: the wetness of the sea, how the mountain was nicer now it was shorter, and what they might do next.

Eventually, Scorpio walked quietly back into the group. He was solid and looked much as they had come to know him. But there was a certain luminous glow to his feathers, and a depth in his bright eyes that caused a new respect in each one who spoke with him. He listened to them and talked about normal things, but he shared a special silence with Pisces. Having Scorpio there again as part of the jostling group, brought a sense of comfort and reassurance into all their hearts.

"As long as Scorpio understands about us all being Love," Cancer explained to Libra, "he can remind us when we forget."

"So we're going to be alright!" sighed Libra with relief.

"ALL right!" said Aquarius, and they all looked at him. "Every one of us – we are ALL right." Then he staggered as Sagittarius slapped him on the back.

"That's a good one!" shouted the centaur, grinning, and they all laughed.

* * *

All around this little world,

the watching stars twinkled with pleasure,

sparkling many colours in celebration.

And the great presence smiled lovingly

throughout its Oneness.

You are love – you are One with all things.

The twelve creatures are all parts of you,

and you have all twelve gifts to give.